Meditations, Poems and Exer
Ease Pregnancy and Birth a
with Their Unborn

Spirit Baby

HELENA CLARE

SPIRIT BABY
Communicate With Your Unborn Baby. Ease Your Birth.
By HELENA CLARE
1. OCC032000 2. HEA041000 3. SEL032000
ISBN: 978-1-949642-45-2
EBOOK: 978-1-949642-46-9

Cover design by LEWIS AGRELL
Interior design by RENEE DURAN

Printed in the United States of America

Authority Publishing
11230 Gold Express Dr. #310-413
Gold River, CA 95670
800-877-1097
www.AuthorityPublishing.com

*To Tariq, celebrating the journey
we made together.*

– Love, your mum. xxx

Introduction

The transformation to first-time mother is among the most magical and sacred journeys that a woman can experience. Preparing for it through meditation, exercise and healthy living can ease potential difficulties and augment this wondrous experience.

More pointedly, connecting with the soul of a child or children before they are born can change a woman's life, as it did mine. This book chronicles my journey from connecting with my spirit baby through to the birth of my son, Tariq, including the poems I wrote for him and the meditations and exercises that helped me communicate with him before he was conceived and to realise my perfect labour.

Along the way, in this book I share what I've learned about communicating with Earth Mother guides, Guardian Angels, and animal spirit guides that immeasurably enrich any woman's experience—during pregnancy and beyond.

As you work through this short book, keep a notebook and pen handy to record your thoughts, insights and messages that your baby and body are communicating to you.

Welcome to my journey.

Contents

Spirit Baby

I wasn't ready for the responsibility
For bringing to this
world a fragile life.
I feared losing my
independence, career, body
And catalysing a marriage of strife

But then I felt a longing
pressing my temples
A yawn awaken in my womb
And overcome by a tearful impulse
Demanded to get pregnant soon.

Months passed, you didn't
grow within me
Tests revealed nothing wanting.
Then I learnt the possibility
you were a spirit baby
And that I could connect with
you through chanting.

So in the smile of an African Sun
I recited those magic sounds.
And a small voice answered
my meditation
With a message that would astound.

"I don't feel you want me,"
 Was your reply, "that's
why I haven't come.

For several years I've been
waiting patiently
For you to invite me
into your home."

"I'm afraid," I admitted.
And told of my fears,
The voice listened calmly and replied
"Still your concerns and
free your tears
For my addition will be the
most joyful of rides.

You'll have an easy
pregnancy and labour too
With no morning sickness
or complications
Your body will bounce back
within a week or two
And I love travel and adventures."

And here I am with you in my arms
My four-hour labour flowed
past like a stream.
You're the cutest babe and
I'm under your charm
As happy as in my most
delectable dream.

Who are you?

Why did you choose us?
What will you teach us?
What will you learn from us?

What are Spirit Babies?

The challenge of the human race is to evolve over time. To enable this, souls are required to return to earth again and again, attempting to overcome specific challenges, learn lessons, or experience life in particular contexts. Before returning to Earth, souls become spirit babies and stay in what can be thought of as a holding bay, where they ready themselves for their new life. Spirit babies choose their parents for specific lessons they can teach or learn, or to fulfil a particular role they have set for themselves.

By connecting with their spirit baby, or babies, parents-to-be can have insights into how to conceive, how to have an easy and healthy pregnancy and a smooth, swift birth. The connection can also enable mothers and couples having difficulty conceiving, to conceive, by providing insights into any concerns the spirit baby may have in coming through to the physical plane.

For a moving book describing this world and providing illuminating case studies, detailed meditations and exercises, read "Spirit Babies," by Walter Makichen.

My husband and I had been trying to conceive for some time without success. On reading "Spirit Babies," I attempted to connect with my spirit baby.

By connecting with their spirit baby, or babies, parents to be can have insights into how to conceive, how to have an easy and healthy pregnancy and a smooth, swift birth.

I was able to do so and the message was clear. The baby didn't feel wanted by me. I discussed my fears with my spirit baby and these fears were allayed. The following month I fell pregnant. Surprisingly, the voice that spoke to me was initially that of a young girl. My baby turned out to be a boy. Given the multiple lives that spirit babies have experienced, they will choose to communicate with you in a persona they feel comfortable with, or that they feel you are comfortable with.

Meditation to your spirit baby

On Why She or He Has Chosen You

Just as we choose our parents, so our spirit babies choose us.
Sometimes the connection is stronger with one parent than the
other. Sometimes it is equally strong with both parents. It may be
that you have known or been related to your spirit baby in a past life.
Understanding why they have chosen us sometimes gives us insight
into how we can support the growth of our babies once they are born.

Relax, sitting upright in a chair with your feet flat on the
floor. Close your eyes and become aware of your breathing.
With each in-breath imagine you are breathing in beautiful
white light. With every out-breath allow your muscles
and your body to relax and let go. Continue to focus on
your breathing until you feel relaxed and at peace.

Imagine tiny golden roots growing out of the
soles of your feet into the earth.

There is a protective silver ball around you; you
are completely safe and looked after.

Now ask to be taken to somewhere where you can meet
with your spirit baby. This may be outer space, a forest,
a beach, anywhere – just see where you are taken.

Then ask for your spirit baby to come and talk with you. The spirit
baby may take many forms such as a baby, a child, a young adult.

Ask your spirit baby why they have chosen you. Is there anything important that you should know, either during the pregnancy, labour or after the birth? Do they have a preference for a name, a colour in the nursery, certain foods that you consume, or guidance for making the labour easier? Ask them if they are happy for you to contact them again. When you have finished, send love to your spirit baby, thank them, and on the third out-breath open your eyes.

Write down what you have learnt. Don't overthink it, just write the first things that come to mind as you write or type.

Yoga Mum

The advert said it's time away
From the hassle and jangle of the day.
Time for the two of us to ponder
On the sacredness of our pregnancy wonder
To relax my nerves and weary body
And connect to my baby just the size of a pea.

But here we are in a flower-scented space
I'm lying prostrate with sun sprinkling on my face.
Around us are eight ladies in various degrees
Of apple, melon or beach ball bellies.
Our three-month-old tummy makes me feel like a fraud
Against nine-month hippos—still moving—I want to applaud!

"Breathe in through your nose so the air expands your chest
With each out-breath let go and sink further into rest.
Become aware of your baby, breath into your womb
Imagine what it's like in that warm, watery room."

The teacher's hypnotic voice carries me inside
To where you play, frolic, somersault and hide.
I can feel your heart beat, know your joy.
Perhaps even tell whether you're a girl or a boy.

You feel safe, I can sense that, and happy too.
"Talk to your baby, she has a message for you."
Sing more to me mummy and eat healthily.
No more fast food, wine or working compulsively.

Is that really you?
Or just my intense desire to believe the voice is true?
Do you feel my every move? Listen to each word I utter?
Hear me and Daddy bicker, taste my breakfast bread and butter?

I'd do everything you ask if I knew the messages were real.
But if I don't and they are, how will you feel?
We start the asanas and you drift deep within.
I'm arching like a cat, breathing my belly in,

Squeezing my pelvic floor muscles, until my eyes pop.
And during the final relaxation start snoring like a sop.
"Thank you," says the teacher, "to all sixteen of you."
I'll change my ways, my miracle, for within me you brew.

A stretch a day keeps the doctor away

Leading a healthy lifestyle is important during pregnancy, to ensure your child has the best start in life, to aid an easy labour, and to give your body the best chance of regaining pre-pregnancy weight and tone quickly. However, take care not to overdo exercise as this can put unnecessary stress on your body.

Yoga is an excellent form of exercise. If possible find a pregnancy yoga class that focuses on safe and effective asanas (positions) and includes visualisations, meditations and techniques to increase the chances of a healthy, natural labour.

Meditation on being with baby in the womb

Either lie on your back or sit cross-legged. Close your eyes.
Become aware of your breath. Slow your breath down to
the count of '4' breathing in and '4' breathing out. Do not
hold your breath but feel it is like the sweep of waves on
the shore, caressing your lips, windpipe and lungs.

Now this time when you breathe in, follow your breath and go
even deeper into your body until you arrive inside your womb.

Imagine what it feels like—warm, watery, dark, safe. What
does your baby feel inside your womb? Does he swim or
somersault around or stay snugly wrapped inside the amniotic
sack? Swim around your baby, feel what he feels, hear what
she hears…the sound of your breathing, your digestive system,
your voice and conversations you have. What does he see?
She can see light and dark through your body walls.

What can he taste when you have sweet or sour food?
Now see if you can talk to your baby. Ask her how she feels, has
she any messages for you? When you are ready swim back up to
consciousness, wiggle your toes, shrug your shoulders and open
your eyes. Write down what happened in your meditation.

Write down what you have learnt. Don't overthink it, just write the first things that come to mind when you write or type.

_____

_____

_____

_____

_____

_____

_____

_____

_____

_____

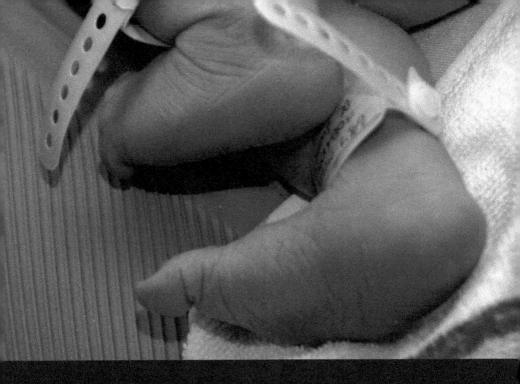

Leaving my print

Like a footprint in moist sand
I leave my print in you.
It stands to reason I want the toes
Grounded and strong
Not gnarled and bent
It's my job to un-scrunch them
before you come.

The spirit baby world

Connection with the spirit baby world reveals that spirits ready to be born into the earthly world, choose their parents. This is sometimes as a gift to one or both parents for something that has happened in a previous life, or because the spirit baby has something to learn from the parents, or the parents to learn from the spirit baby. It is also sometimes to balance karma. Think of karma as an exchange of energy.

To evolve spiritually, we need to balance our karma from previous lifetimes; this can be done through agreements made with other souls before we are born and experienced on Earth. Spirit babies choose their parents. Whether you are same-gender parents, biological parents, step-parents or adoptive parents you can connect with your spirit baby and call them to you. Often, this union has been agreed to even before the parents' birth in the spirit world. It is sacred and should be honoured for the spirit contract it is.

Understanding why we have chosen our parents can shed light on challenges we have that may be holding back our full spiritual development or our contentment and happiness. By understanding and learning from the relationship we have with our parents we can become better parents ourselves. Negative emotions that we hold onto with our own parents can affect our relationship with our own children. In this meditation we imagine meeting our parents, in their purest form, if only the best parts of them were present. We call this a person's 'highest self,' their purest form; one can also say it is their 'soul'.

Meditation on finding why you chose your parents

Lie, or sit comfortably with your back straight. Close your eyes. Relax. Feel yourself becoming heavier and sinking into the ground. Imagine you are falling slowly through the earth and consecutive layers of worlds until you arrive in a grassy meadow.

The sun is warm but not too hot and dances on your bare arms. To your right is a gently meandering river. Feel the grass underneath your feet and smell the fragrance of summer flowers. You walk towards the river and sit on the bank watching the water drift by.

Soon you see the front of a small wooden boat coming towards you from the right. The boat is propelled by its own silent power; in the boat is the 'highest self' of your birth mother, gleaming with a beautiful light and full of calmness and composure. The boat pulls into the bank beside you and she steps from the boat to stand with you. This is the purest form of your mother; all that is good in her is reflected in this presence before

you. Ask her why you chose her to be your birth mother in this life.

Listen carefully to what she says. Ask her any questions you want. If you are angry or unhappy about any particular incidents in your past, raise them with her now and when she responds imagine white light shining from your own body onto her highest self. This white light is forgiveness. When you've asked her all the questions you can think of, thank her. She returns to the boat, which drifts away downstream and around the bend in the river.

Next along the river from the right side comes another boat. This boat carries the highest self of your birth father. He also gleams with light. He alights beside you. Ask your birth father why you chose him in this life and discuss any emotions you have connected with him. Thank him for helping to teach you and send him forgiving white light. Let him depart along the river.

Write down what you have learnt and how this sheds light on the events of your life so far and what negative emotions you should let go of to be a more whole person and parent for your child.

I start the day with you

You are my treasure chest
My lemon zest
My reason my arrow
My blood bones and marrow
You are my bundle of joy
My beautiful boy
The pigment of the sun
My beloved one.

Connecting with your unborn baby through song

By 17 weeks unborn babies can already hear the sound of the mother's heartbeat, bodily functions and loud noises from outside the body. They can hear the voice of their mothers clearly through the body and also from outside through the stomach wall.

It has also been discovered that babies' learning begins in the womb. In your last trimester take time to consciously sing to your baby. Make up rhymes or songs to them that you sing in the shower or in the car. Before you go to bed at night, repeat a favourite lullaby—when your baby is born s/he will associate this song with sleep and you can use it to help them relax. If you have a partner or close relative, ask them to frequently talk to the baby, close to your abdomen.

My son's father spoke to our son every night during my pregnancy, putting his face close to my tummy. When our son was born, as soon as his father spoke his face showed instant recognition and he clasped his father's finger.

The wonder of you

As fragile as a butterfly's antennae
As ancient as the mountains
As cosmic as the universe
As sacred as a child's prayer
As familiar as the sun
As unknown as the ocean's floor
I welcome you into my heart, my life

What's in a name?

Many spirit babies have a particular preference when
it comes to their name. Asking your baby if he has a
preference is an important bonding exercise and can help
you identify the perfect name for your loved one.

When I was carrying my son we had narrowed the names
to two, Tariq and Aadam, but I wanted our son to have
a choice over his name. He had told me that he preferred
the name Tariq. But we wanted some way of confirming
I had understood correctly. When I met with him in
meditation he clearly stated his preference was for Tariq.

A couple of months later I attended a friend's wedding
in La Gomera. During the stay another guest who was a
psychic specialising in contact with unborn babies asked
me if I would like her to contact my unborn baby. I asked
if she could shed light on my son's preferred name.

Without discussing with her our preferences she said that she
was being told the name had an "R" and a "Q" in it. We told her
that Tariq seemed to be our son's preferred choice. Surprised, she
informed us a spirit called Tariq has been calling her for several
months. She also said that Tariq had told her he had already informed
me that 'Tariq' was his preferred choice, which of course he had.

In many religions such as Islam, the name given to a child is
important. Tariq means "morning star" or "pathway to the light".
Our morning star was born at 8.20 am after a smooth labour.

Meditation on consulting your spirit baby on a preferred name

Lie on your back and with each breath relax further into the ground. Ask to be taken to a place that your spirit baby feels comfortable in. It could be a grassy meadow or a shaded forest, or a beach beside turquoise water.

Ask your spirit baby if he or she has a preferred name. If you have a name in mind, discuss it. Be aware of any sensations you feel when you say the name you are suggesting. Your spirit baby may communicate through sensations, your gut instinct through dreams, mental images or words.

When you have concluded the meditation send love to your spirit baby, thank them for talking to you, and on the third in-breath open your eyes. Write down any ideas of names that have come to you either in this meditation or over the next few weeks.

Connecting with your Spirit Baby – stories

In this section we share inspirational experiences from other women.

Jennifer's Story

I vividly recall an experience I had while 8 months pregnant during a weekend retreat with my spiritual women's group. There were two of us pregnant at the same time, and we were the first to become mothers in the group. We decided to do a ritual where we could all hold sacred space together and allow each of us to share/pray/express our deepest concerns and vision for a healthy and beautiful birth. It was a beautiful and intimate experience for all of us. I had a sense that something was opening up in my awareness as I allowed myself to express with complete vulnerability my hopes and fears about this baby. After this ritual, we danced together and I received the most clear and direct images about this baby being a little red-headed girl. Although I knew the sex of the baby, I felt unsettled that I didn't have a sense of her. She showed me that her light was strong and bright. That she was on purpose. That she was unique and outstanding in every way – exemplified by her locks of curly red hair. The clarity of this vision and the connection it made me feel at the time played out strongly as she was born and grew into herself. All of the intuitive information that moment held for me was fully expressed after her birth. I strongly believe it was a matter of giving myself permission to receive whatever I needed for the perfect birth, in the polarity of my own courage and vulnerability and then from there, I was gifted with the connection to such clear information about her. What a sacred and delightful experience.

Renee's Story

Three years before my baby was born, she somehow told me that she was going to be a girl, and that she would be born in May. Each year, when I hadn't conceived in August (9 months before May), I was confused. After trying to have a baby for 3 years, I decided to try adoption. As soon as I signed up with an agency, a woman picked me who was carrying a boy. Again, I was confused, but figured I just didn't hear spirit right. After the boy was born, the birth mother changed her mind. The following month I was introduced to another woman who was to give birth in May. As soon as I met her, she said. "I'm sure I am carrying this baby for you." I was sure also. Two months after that, my healthy beautiful daughter was born, and a long time friendship began with her birth mother. My daughter continued to communicate with me psychically until she learned to speak well enough to get all her thoughts through. But that's another story.

Lynn's Story

I'd like to share my story as an "adoptive grandmother". A few years ago I was awakened during the night with what I knew was a message from spirit. I knew it was because I had been receiving messages from spirit this way ever since I received my first one, in October, 1987. I also knew from experience that I had to get up and write it down, before I'd forget it. This is the message I received on 7-5-2011, "Something amazing, wonderful and beautiful is about to happen to him. He's going to his forever home." The next morning I looked at what I wrote and I had absolutely no idea what that meant, but I knew I would find out, soon, of that I had no doubt. That very afternoon my oldest daughter Aubrey called me to say that she and her husband had some exciting news that they had been keeping a secret until it was official; they were given permission to adopt another child (they had already adopted 3 children from all different nationalities and also had one biological child), a 4 year old boy from an orphanage in China! His birth mother had left him at an orphanage the morning he was born, with severe facial deformities. Hudson, as we call him, has had several corrective surgeries and will have several more, but in spite of all this, he is a very smart, sweet and loving 10 year old boy who has been part of our family since 2011.

My body is not my own

My body has been hijacked
My brain completely side-tracked
By a hormone tsunami
This isn't me!

My ankles are my gran's
My breasts are frying pans.
My puffy fingers are bear paws
My gums bleeding horror jaws.

My stomach is a seasick sailor
My once rosy pallor couldn't be paler.
All night my legs throb like a marathon athlete
My mid-rift needs a pillow as do my bloated feet.

What next?
I already can't contemplate sex!
Do stretch marks threaten?
Do killer kilograms beckon?

But baby I don't care.
When I imagine the silkiness of your hair
The colour of your eyes,
The vulnerability of your size
I'm the luckiest mum in the world.

Connecting with our bodies

Our bodies perform an amazing service in giving birth to our babies. Labour is demanding mentally, emotionally and physically. By working in advance to connect with our bodies we can help prepare ourselves better for labour, undertaking the necessary exercises that will help prepare vital body parts such as the cervix, perineum and womb.

During the birthing process by connecting with key body parts and listening to their advice you can smooth the birthing process. Whether heard through an inner voice or instinctively understood, listening to your body can shorten labour times and help you make crucial decisions during the birthing process such as when to go to hospital, or when to push so as not to tear.

In the six month of pregnancy I began connecting with different parts of my body. I would relax with my eyes closed and focus on the body part I wanted to communicate with. Then I'd simply ask it questions. To my surprise different body parts answered in different voices, some male, others female, even my breasts had distinctly different voices.

During the early stages of active labour I asked my cervix how dilated she was. "Five centimetres", she replied. After consciously willing her to open up like petals of a flower bud an hour later I asked her again how dilated she was, "eight centimetres", came the reply. at which point I decided it was time to get to the hospital. Twenty minutes later, on arrival, the mid-wife examined me. "Fantastic, you're eight centimetres dilated!"

Preparing for an easy labour

I've rarely known people to be so willing to
impart bad news as when I was pregnant.
In particular, women relished traumatic labour stories.
Pregnancy and labour can be a very empowering experience
for you and it is important to take care of which
thoughts, images and fears you identify with so you
can prepare yourself emotionally as well as physically,
logistically and mentally, for the labour.

If possible, surround yourself with stories of positive pregnancy
and labour experiences. Whilst you have to be aware of what can
go wrong and make necessary provision, focus on having a positive
pregnancy and labour experience. This will make you calmer and
more likely to have a smooth experience. I focused on having a
smooth, swift, four-hour labour. For neither of my two births did I
take a paracetamol or painkillers. And each was less than four hours.

Logistics

Choose the hospital, obstetrician and midwives with whom you feel comfortable and that resonate with your preferred birth approach. If possible hire a doula (birth assistant) who will help you plan your perfect labour and assist you during birth with natural pain relief skills.

Do you want a water birth or music or candles during labour? It is a sacred time for you and your birth partner to enable your baby's passage from spirit baby world to earth. Make it what you want. If you have limited choice because of restrictions placed on you by the health system in your country, be creative in the areas you do have control over. Also have your hospital bag waiting at least two weeks in advance just in case baby comes early!

Some mothers are wedded to a natural birth, while others prefer a caesarean birth. I was very committed to natural birthing and surprised when a friend of mine who was very in touch with her body, opted for an elective caesarean. A couple of years after her son was born, she discovered she had a weak heart valve and had to have open heart surgery. The physical exertion needed in natural labour could have caused a heart attack.

Our bodies are incredibly wise; we just need to listen to them. Our higher guidance and that given by our spiritual guides form a powerful support system that we can call on in pregnancy and labour. In the next sections we provide meditations that enable you to connect with these loving and wise supporters.

The Red Hibiscus

Scarlet petals tucked into your bud
Open for baby.
Wide like a yawn
Welcoming a soul's new dawn.
Flexible, strong, the colour
of life and health
Beautiful entrance to a world of love
and nature's wealth.

Meditation to connect with your cervix

Sit comfortably upright on a chair, on the floor with
your legs crossed, or, lie on your back with your
arms and legs slightly apart from your body.
Breathe in to the count of four and out to the count of
six; continue to breathe in and out to this rhythm. Each
time you breathe out feel yourself sinking more
deeply into the floor. Feel the backs of your legs, buttocks,
spine, head and arms supported by the ground beneath you.

Now focus on your cervix. Send her greetings. Thank her for the
work she is about to do during labour, opening up around your
baby, and ask her if there is anything you can do to help her quickly
and easily dilate during labour. Ask her if there is a particular flower
that she would like you to visualise when asking her to open up?
Or a particular image like a door opening up? Now focus on your
perineum, ask her if there is anything that you can do for her?
What about massage? Affirm that she is strong and
flexible. Imagine that she is an elastic band that will
easily stretch open and then spring back into shape.
You can make contact with your other body parts in
this manner before, during and after birth.

Make sure you thank your body for the work it does for you. A loved
body is a happy body and a happy body tends to be a healthy body.

Exercise

Close your eyes. With your legs crossed and your back against the wall, breathe in as you tighten your pelvic floor muscles (these are the muscles that you hold to stop urination in mid-flow). Pull them up all the way to your navel, then while breathing out hold them tight. Breathe in once more. Now imagine your cervix is a beautiful flower in bud. As you breathe out, imagine this bud opening up petal by petal as you relax the muscles, until the flower is completely open and your pelvic floor muscles are completely relaxed. Repeat 20 times.

Connecting with your 'spirit' birth supporters

During pregnancy and labour, communicate with your spirit baby and other birth supporters such as your Earth Mother guide, Guardian Angel and animal spirit guides can contribute to a comfortable pregnancy and smooth labour.

Every woman has an Earth Mother guide, who has the wisdom of all your birth experiences throughout different lifetimes. With the help of your Earth Mother guide, even with your first labour you have the knowledge to ensure a smooth, self-assured labour, drawing on your past experiences. The Earth Mother guide can be called on to help guide your spirit baby from the spirit baby world into the Earthly world. Just invite her to join you when you are meditating and ask her; she will be very happy to assist you.

Your animal spirit guides may be with you for life or for a period of time spanning a particular stage or issue in your life. Animal guides bring particular knowledge or boost a need that you may have at a particular time such as courage, fortitude, or confidence. Discuss with your animal guides what role they will play in supporting you. Contact your Earth Mother and animal guides as you would contact your Guardian Angel in the following exercise. As you meditate and connect with your various guides more regularly, you will eventually be able to communicate with them instantaneously, as part of your "conscious" day.

Planning your labour date with your spirit baby

Connecting with your spirit baby is also very useful to fine-tune your labour and pregnancy. Like a team, you can plan together how to make your labour smoother and reassure each other during the birth.

I frequently talked to Tariq and my second child, Saafi, during pregnancy and labour. About two weeks before Tariq's due date, on Friday 12th September, I asked him when he would be coming.

"Soon," he replied.

"Can I go to Ade and Anna's party tomorrow night"? I asked him, not knowing how soon was soon!

"Yes," he replied, "but have your hospital bag ready".

"OK…and can I help Fatima pack for her house move on Sunday?"

"No mum, you need to rest," came the reply.

On the Sunday morning I asked him again, "When will you come?"

"I will be arriving tomorrow", he replied.

I was shocked. I had visitors coming that evening for a meal. Fortunately they went home early and by 10 pm I was feeling the early signs of labour. I checked in again with Tariq.

"I'll arrive around 8 am tomorrow morning", he said. He arrived at 8.20 am on Monday 15th September.

Saafi was also very clear what I should and shouldn't do. Two weeks before my due date it was Eid, and we were due to spend the day with my sister in law, in a neighbouring city one hour's drive away, but Saafi insisted I stay close to home and rest. My water broke that night.

Communicating with my unborn boys helped me plan my labours and ensure I wasn't faced with any early birth surprises.

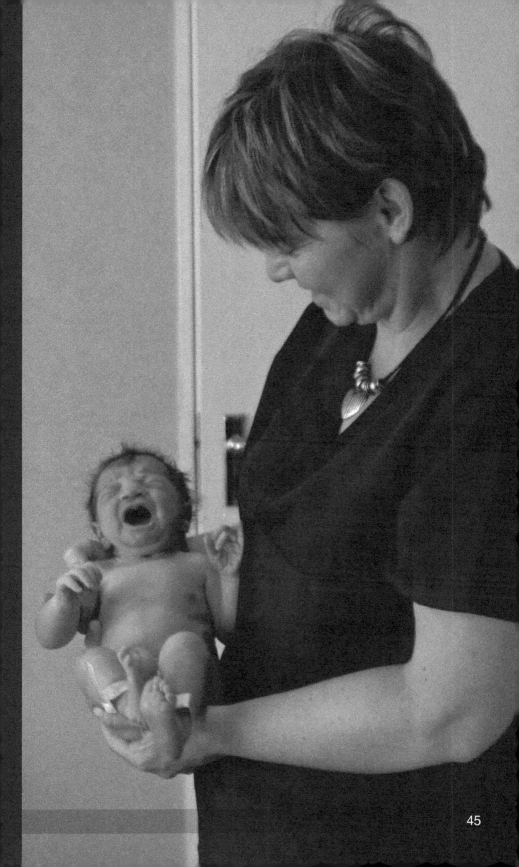

Angel Blessing

Wings of light
Omniscient sight
Pure of heart
Of God a part
Bless our baby.
Create a golden passageway within me.
Through which he can pass safely,
Smoothly, swiftly, painlessly.
Thank you.

Meditation for connecting with your Guardian Angel

Everyone has a guardian angel that is with them for their whole lives. Some people can communicate easily with their guardian angel, through dreams, inner voices, inner visions and 'instinct'. Some people can smell or see lights when their guardian angel is around. It may take some time and attempts to communicate with your Guardian Angel but with perseverance they will be one of the wisest, most reliable and unwavering supports you have in your life, and can be called on day and night. For more information on how to connect with your Guardian Angel and guides, and on how to become a light worker, check out my book *The Lightseeker's Manual.*

A guardian angel can appear in many forms. During pregnancy and labour your Guardian Angel is wonderful to answer questions and concerns you may have and to give guidance for your best and highest good (your best possible decisions or course in life). With practice you will be able to contact your Guardian Angel quickly and in any context. Following is a simple visualisation to start your connection.

Sit in a comfortable chair with your feet flat on the floor and your spine upright. Close your eyes. Become aware of your breathing. Breathe in deeply to the count of four and out to the count of four. When you breathe in imagine you are breathing in gleaming white light through the base of your feet. It flows through your body filling you with a warm clean sensation. When you breathe out breathe the white light out of the top of your head along with any negative thoughts or toxins. Continue this relaxing breath for several minutes. Now imagine you are in the most beautiful place you can conceive of—somewhere in your dreams you'd love to live. This is your spirit home. It is a place you always feel safe, supported and at ease. Here only people and spirits whom you invite are able to come.

Feel the ground beneath your feet, study the details around you, note the smells and sounds. Now ask your Guardian Angel to make him or herself present to you. S/he may appear as a light, a person, a feeling, even a voice. Thank your Guardian Angel for supporting you in this lifetime. You can ask whatever questions you wish, e.g., who s/he is, what your mission in life is, or questions about your pregnancy. Ask them how you can prepare for an easier labour. Listen and give thanks to your Guardian Angel; know they will always be with you and can be called upon at any time.

When you are ready on the third breath, open your eyes and record any impressions or guidance you have received.

_____

_____

_____

_____

_____

_____

_____

_____

_____

_____

_____

_____

_____

_____

_____

_____

_____

_____

_____

_____

_____

_____

_____

_____

Create a vision board

Vision boards are powerful tools to focus your mind and energy during pregnancy and your life in general. It directs your attention and energy to your heart's desires.

Find a large piece of colourful card or paper. Onto it stick photos, pictures or cutouts from magazines that represent your hopes and dreams for pregnancy, labour and motherhood. Place it somewhere you frequently look—on your wardrobe door or bedroom wall, or above the mirror where you brush your teeth.

As you look at the pictures imagine the sensations you will feel when these hopes come true. The more often and intensely you imagine these feelings the stronger the energy of attraction you create to make them happen. You can also draw a symbolic picture of your perfect labour, placing it somewhere you look often.

Tracy Donegan - midwife and founder of GentleBirth (www.gentlebirth.com)

Draw your perfect birth

Imagery is powerful in preparing yourself for your perfect birth and maximising the chances of it happening. Visualising my perfect birth was a key part of preparing me for my labour. I painted a picture of how I saw my perfect birth. I imagined myself as a tunnel of golden light that reached from heaven through my womb and birth canal. I imagined it expanding easily to allow my baby smoothly through. I repeated the affirmation 'Make me a tunnel of golden light'.

I also had the image of the powerful and ancient trees of La Gomera with their roots drawing my baby through me into this earthly world. Finally, in preparation for my birth, I frequently imagined my cervix opening up like the petals of a beautiful red hibiscus flower. These images filled me with love for my body, the birthing process, and the receipt of my spirit baby.

Set aside an hour or so to draw or paint your perfect birth. Go wild, add glitter and bright beautiful colours, or do whatever you like to create something that reflects your ideal birth!

Affirmations, visualisations and sound

Embrace positive stories of labour and ignore those that are negative. Even if your mother had a difficult labour with you, it does not mean yours will be difficult. Use affirmations for a positive pregnancy and birth. You can create your own birth process; do not be scared but be confident that whatever experience you have—whether natural, accompanied by external assistance or a caesarean—it will be the right experience for you. Sometimes although we don't wish it, a challenging experience is necessary for us to grow.

Repeat affirming affirmations such as "My labour will be smooth, swift and safe"; "I am 100% supported throughout my pregnancy and labour by divine wisdom and love."

Throughout my pregnancy I constantly repeated positive affirmations to myself including "I will have a smooth, swift, safe and natural labour of less than four hours." I was fortunate enough to have just that both times, with no painkillers, or any artificial support.

Before the labour, decide what visualisations you are going to use. Visualisations can be very powerful. For many people the image of contractions as waves passing over them can relieve some of the pain. I imagined a golden passageway was opening up within me through which my baby would pass. With each contraction I'd imagine this golden tunnel getting wider.

Sound can also be a strong pain reliever. Releasing a full-chested note during the contraction can have the effect of pricking the "pain balloon" of the contraction. This was particularly useful for me during the mid-stages of labour. Some pregnancy yoga classes will incorporate sound into labour planning.

Adventures together

You are our new adventure
And together we'll seek adventure
Whether in the long ferns of a Cornish moor
Or the shade of Table Mountain, along Cape Town's shore.
In the lapping waters of an azure African sea
Or under the sunny dapple of a La Gomeran tree.
Or simply being there when you utter your first word
Hearing you chortle at our favourite garden birds
Together smelling nature's first spring flower
Spying your face as you taste sweet and sour.
All this we'll enjoy with you.
Our child, our playmate, our love most true.

Wishing you all the joy for a marvellous adventure with your new child.

ABOUT HELENA CLARE

 Raised in Cornwall UK, Helena has lived in Indonesia, Fiji and South Africa. She is an environmental economist and international development leader, managing aid programmes focused on uplifting the poorest countries and their people in Africa and globally. She is also a Kahuna masseur, kinesciologist and angel and ascension teacher. Helena is the author of *The Lightseeker's Manual - How to Communicate with Angels, Raise Your Vibrations and Save the World and The Spiritual Side of Disability – How to Thrive with a Special Needs Child.*

Helena is mum to two beautiful boys, Tariq and Saafi, who are the delight and joy of her life. She is passionate about finding solutions to the world's most critical challenges and empowering people to find their own *highest paths*. She currently lives in South Africa with her two sons.

FREE MEDITATION

To download your free audio meditation
"Connecting with Your Spirit Baby" – visit
https://lightseekersway.com/sb-meditation/

ACKNOWLEDGEMENTS

Thank you to my two beautiful sons Tariq and Saafi
who have taught me so much about spirit babies.

Thank you to my amazing midwives Heather Pieterse, Margot
Ludik, Christel Jordaan and my super special doula Marie-
Louise Steyn for supporting my smooth, sacred births.

And my heart felt gratitude to Mosebjadi Ledwaba, Esti Viljoen
and *Miya Photography* for their exquisite photographs.

Thank you to Stephanie at Authority Publishing and her wonderful
team, to Renee for her interior design and inspiration, to Wendy
for early review of the draft and to all my amazing family and
friends for their love and encouragement in my writing.

CONNECT ON SOCIAL MEDIA

Twitter: Helena Clare @LightseekersWay
Facebook: The Lightseeker's Way
Instagram: helenaclare.lightseekersway
Website: www.LightseekersWay.com

CONTACT HELENA

Contact Helena about speaking engagements, media appearances or just to say hello at www.LightseekersWay.com and email helena@lightseekersway.com.

CPSIA information can be obtained
at www.ICGtesting.com
Printed in the USA
BVHW090754060822
643899BV00011B/755